SCHUBERT

GW00835914

Moments Musicaux
D.780

Edited and annotated by
HOWARD FERGUSON

THE ASSOCIATED BOARD OF
THE ROYAL SCHOOLS OF MUSIC

Uniform with this edition

SCHUBERT

edited by Howard Ferguson

Complete Pianoforte Sonatas

(including the unfinished works)

Volumes I, II & III

Variations, D.156 & 576

Fantasy in C ('The Wanderer'), D.760

Moments Musicaux, D.780

Four Impromptus, D.899

Four Impromptus, D.935

Three Piano Pieces, D.946

Nine Short Piano Pieces

Thirty-three Dances

CONTENTS

INTRODUCTION

Sources

A   Autograph: lost.

B   MS copy of No.3, with the title 'Air russe', once the property of Schubert's friend Albert Stadler. (Lund, Universitetsbibliothek, Taussig Collection.)

C   1st edition of No.3, with the title 'Air russe': *Album musicale,* I, pp.13-15; Sauer & Leidesdorf, Vienna [1823], Plate No.490.

D   1st edition of No.6, with the title 'Plaintes d'un Troubadour': *Album musicale,* II, pp.22-25; Sauer & Leidesdorf, Vienna [1824], Plate No.590.

Both C & D were reprinted in *La Guirlande,* I; Sauer & Leidesdorf, Vienna [1825].

E   1st complete edition: *Momens Musicals [sic] pour le Piano Forte par François Schubert. Oeuvre 94.* Cahier I, II; M. J. Leidesdorf, Vienna [1828], Plate Nos.1043, 1044.

The present edition follows E and refers to C & D.

The Text

Since the autograph is lost, the text is based of necessity on secondary sources, i.e. the early editions, C, D & E, listed above. As far as notes are concerned they are fairly free from obvious misprints, apart from the eight listed in the footnotes. In other respects they copy a number of Schubert's notational idiosyncracies concerning slurs and ties, dynamics, and accidentals.

Slurs and ties. At times Schubert drew slurs so carelessly that it is impossible to tell where they are meant to begin and end. This probably explains E's inconsistent phrasing in No.4, bb.62-68, where in some bars the initial slur ends on the second note, in others on the third, and in one instance is missing altogether. In such cases an editor must do his best to decide what was intended; but it is as well to remember that there is no guarantee that his decisions are correct. It is also useful to remember that Schubert, like most classical composers, often used slurs to divide a long legato phrase into shorter units, each generally ending at a barline. This does not necessarily imply a break in the legato, as can be seen from No.1, bb.30-33.

When tying one chord to another Schubert habitually left out some of the necessary signs. Provided the chords are identical his meaning is likely to be clear, as can be seen from No.2, r.h. bb.57-58, where editorial ties are marked with a cross-stroke. When the chords are not identical, however, his intentions are less certain. For example, in No.6, b.61, the r.h. B(flat) should, strictly speaking, be restruck for the chord is *slurred* to the one before, not tied; yet the ties to the l.h. E(flat)s, and (by implication) to the B(flat)s, suggest that there should also be a tie to the r.h. B(flat)s. Here and in similar passages the player should feel free to disagree with the editor's decisions.

Dynamics. Schubert was far less careful about dynamic markings than, say, Beethoven. For example, his accent (>) is often indistinguishable from a 'hairpin' *dim.* (⊳). In No.1, b.2, the sign here shown as > could equally well have been intended as ⊳ . Though this is probably the only instance in the *Moments Musicaux* of this particular ambiguity, it is as well to remember that any printed accent in a work by Schubert *may* be the editor's misreading of ⊳ , and *vice versa*.

Another ambiguous mark is the compound sign *fp* ⊲ , shown in No.6, b.7. Paul Badura-Skoda has suggested that it probably means *f* ⊳ *p*; and although no proof exists, this may well be so.

At times Schubert's dynamics are so sparse that it is essential to supplement them. In No.6, for example, it is obvious that bb.90-91 should have the same ⊲ ⊳ as the exactly parallel bb.82-83. Less obviously, in No.3 an editorial *p* seems to be needed in b.41, otherwise the *dim.* in bb.41 & 45 would be quite impractical after the *ppp* in b.39.

Accidentals. Schubert's notation of accidentals was always idiosyncratic and often careless. When a passage extends over more than a seventh in a single bar, as in No.4, r.h. b.13, he generally writes the necessary accidental(s) only in the first octave. Moreover, he sometimes expects accidentals to remain in force across the barline (No.5, r.h. bb.42-43 & l.h. bb.56-57), forgets them altogether (No.4, r.h. F in b.78), or writes the wrong one (No.4, r.h. F in b.80: see the footnote). In the *Moments Musicaux,* however, there is never any doubt about the reading intended.

Pedalling

The only pedal marks in the sources are the *Ped.* in No.4, bb.22 & 124 – and even these seem to be inaccurately placed (see the footnote to b.22). Since no editorial marks have been added, the player must decide for himself where, and how much, additional pedalling is required – always remembering that frequent changes of pedal are more likely to suit Schubert's music than the long, impressionistic 'washes' of pedal so often needed in later piano writing.

Tempo

In Nos.1, 3 & 5 only a single basic tempo is needed, apart from the normal small *rits.* and rubatos. But the more varied moods of Nos.2, 4 & 6 require greater flexibility. The following suggestions are in no way authoritative, but may prove helpful if only as points of departure:

No.1, Moderato [♩ = c.96].

No.2, Andantino [♩. = c.54]; b.18*f* [♩. = c.60]; b.56*f* [♩. = c.66].

No.3, Allegro moderato (in source C, Allegretto moderato) [♩ = c.92].

No.4, Moderato [♩ = c.96]; b.62*f* [♩ = c.84].

No.5, Allegro vivace [♩ = c.100].

No.6, Allegretto [♩ = c.120, but flexible].

Staccato Dots (•) and Wedges (▼)

These two signs are clearly differentiated in Schubert's autographs; and although often misinterpreted in early editions, their use in the *Moments Musicaux* seems authentic. The wedge only appears in No.5, bb.20-21, 31 & 33, while the dot is used elsewhere. It seems likely that Schubert used the wedge in its pre-Beethoven sense of an accent, either with or without staccato, while the dot already had its present-day meaning. He was far from consistent, however, as can be seen from the presence of wedges in No.5, bb.20-21 and their absence in the exactly parallel bb.95-96.

Rhythmic Conventions

Another early practice followed by Schubert was the convention of adjusting dotted rhythms in duple time to coincide with triplets when the two occurred simultaneously. One passage in the *Moments Musicaux* is of special interest in this connection, since its interpretation remains in doubt. In the first half of No.1 (bb.1-29) duple and triple rhythms alternate constantly; but as they never actually occur together, it seems likely that each should be played exactly as written. In bb.38-49 of the middle section, however, the two rhythms *do* appear simultaneously; and this suggests that here the r.h. semiquavers should be adjusted to coincide with the 3rd quaver of each l.h. triplet. But a doubt remains: for the r.h. part of bb.38-49 is a development of b.37, which is in true duple rhythm. This being so, it is arguable that duple rhythm should persist in the r.h. throughout bb.38-49, in spite of the pull of the l.h. triplets. Each player must decide for himself which interpretation he prefers.

Ornamentation

The only ornaments used in the *Moments Musicaux* are single small notes and pairs of small notes.

Single small note: ♪. In E these are always shown as ♪, which formerly was one way of notating an isolated semiquaver. The form ♪ has been preferred in the present edition, not only because it was the one generally used by Schubert, but also because it appears in both C & D.

Regarding the interpretation of the sign, Paul Badura-Skoda has pointed out that a single small note in the voice part of a Schubert song often stands for a long appoggiatura, whereas the same appoggiatura is shown in the piano accompaniment at its true value, i.e. as a normal-sized note. Hence it would appear that in the piano works a single small note (of whatever value) is usually intended to be a short, unaccented acciaccatura (the present-day ♪). Occasionally however – as in

No.6, b.73, and possibly in No.2, bb.16 & 81, the context suggests that a single small note, even in a piano work, is probably intended as an expressively accentuated appoggiatura *on* the beat.

Pairs of small notes: ♫. It would seem from the contexts that all pairs of small notes in the *Moments Musicaux* should anticipate the beat.

Practice

The only one of the six pieces that is really awkward technically is No.5. When practising it begin by taking the main subject thus:

$$\frac{2}{4} \; \text{♩ ♩ | ♩ ♫ | ♩ ♩ | ♩ ♫ |} \; \text{etc.}$$

This allows one time to define and prepare for the precise hand- and finger-movements needed in order to reach each accented chord accurately. The pairs of quavers should be thought of as 'upbeats' leading to the following crotchet.

This Edition

In the present edition numbered footnotes are concerned with textual matters, and lettered footnotes with the interpretation of ornaments, etc. Redundant accidentals have been omitted. Editorial accidentals, notes, rests, dynamics, etc., are printed either in small type or within square brackets, and editorial slurs, ties, and 'hairpin' *cresc.* and *dim.* signs are crossed with a small vertical line. Curved brackets indicate that a note should not be struck. The fingering throughout is editorial, as there is none in the sources.

Schubert's distribution of notes on the two staves appears to have been dictated by scribal convenience rather than musical considerations: like many earlier composers his aim was to avoid, so far as possible, leger-lines and clef changes. The result is often confusing for the player: for at times the whole texture is crammed on to a single stave, and chords and melodies lose their visual shape through being divided between the two staves. The editor has therefore felt free to alter the layout whenever doing so might make it easier to read. Generally his aim has been to place r.h. notes on the upper stave and l.h. notes on the lower; but occasionally it has been more convenient to use the signs ⌊ and ⌈ to indicate the r.h. and l.h. respectively.

My thanks are due to the British Library Board for providing microfilms of the 1st editions, and for their permission to make use of them for this edition.

HOWARD FERGUSON
Cambridge 1979

MOMENTS MUSICAUX

D. 780

SCHUBERT, Op. 94
? 1823-1828

(a) gracenotes before the beat.

A.B. 1769

(b) see the Introduction under Rhythmic Conventions.

1) B.67: though this *da capo* is printed in full in the 1st edition, it is unlikely that Schubert wrote it out in the autograph.
His usual practice was to put 'D.C.' or 'D.C. al segno' at the appropriate point, then add the Coda if it was required (here there is none).

Andantino

(a) gracenotes before the beat.   *(b)* possibly

1) Bb.16 & 81, r.h. lowest line, note 3: the *Gesammtausgabe* (1888) and many later editions change these unnecessarily to respectively A (flat) & E (flat).

A.B.1769

2) B. 46, l.h. beat 1: E has a redundant semibreve E (flat) below the stave.
3) B. 49, l.h. beat 2: E has a redundant minim C above the stave.

4) B. 54, l.h. lower line, note 1: E mistakenly has F, not E (flat).
5) B. 65, r.h: notes 1 & 2 are tied in E; but see the more probable b. 27.

(c) see footnote *(b)*.

6) B.78: in E r.h. lowest line, note 4 is C, not F; and l.h. chord 4 is octave E (flat), not D natural; but see b.13.

Allegro moderato [1]

(a) gracenotes before the beat; in b. 4 probably with the A (flat) s tied – though in C the slurs all end on the B (flat).

1) B.1: in C the tempo mark is 'Allegretto moderato'.

2) B.18, l.h. chords 2 & 4: thus in C; E mistakenly adds A (flat) below the C.

3) B. 24, r.h: thus in C; E mistakenly places the crotchet tail on the 2nd F.

A.B.1769

4) B.32: the hairpin *dim.* is in C, but not in E.

Moderato

1) B. 22, etc: thus in E: but the 𝄢 should probably be under beat 1.

A.B.1769

2) Bb. 62-68, r.h: the first slur in most of these bars is carried on to the crotchet – probably a misreading of the notation shown.

3) B. 80, r.h. upper line, note 1: E has a flat to the F, which is most improbable (see the equivalent bb. 86 & 88). The F in b.78 has no accidental.

A.B.1769

4) Bb.103-163: this D.C. is printed in full in E, though it is unlikely that Schubert would have bothered to write it out. He would simply have added the Coda after b.61, in the same way that he did in the Impromptu in A flat, D.935/2, and the letters D.C. after b.102.

A.B.1769

Allegro vivace

A. B. 1769

2) B.96: it seems likely that the repeat of the 2nd half should be from the end of b.96 rather than the end of b.111, though the latter is shown in E. Bars 97-111 then become a coda.

3) B.104, l.h. middle line, chords 2 & 3: E mistakenly has G, not F.

4) Bb.106 & 108: E has staccato dots, not wedges.

A.B.1769

Allegretto

(a) gracenotes before the beat.

1) Bb.53-57: the slurs and ties are garbled in both E & D; the present version follows bb.8-12.

26

TRIO

Allegretto D.C.